FIELD EDUCATIONAL
PUBLICATIONS, INC.
A Subsidiary of Field Enterprises, Inc.

609 Mission Street, San Francisco,
California 94105

Submitted for Reading and
American History

AMERICANS ALL SERIES

Elementary-Secondary Supplementary
Grades 5-8
Eight Texts, One Teacher's Manual

RETURN POSTAGE GUARANTEED

CHUMASH BOY

CHUMASH BOY

Curr
428.4
F457a
no.1

WITHDRAWN FROM
SUU LIBRARY

John Rambeau
Professor of Education
Director, Reading Laboratory
Northern Arizona University

Nancy Rambeau

Richard E. Gross
Professor of Education
Stanford University

SUSC Curriculum
Library

illustrations
Sabina & Jean Yates

FIELD EDUCATIONAL PUBLICATIONS, INC. • SAN FRANCISCO

Copyright © 1968 by
FIELD EDUCATIONAL PUBLICATIONS, INC.
All rights reserved. This volume may not be reproduced in whole or
in part in any form without written permission from the publishers.
Printed in U.S.A.

A
VANISHED
TRIBE

IT IS fairly certain that the Indians came to North America from Asia. There was once a bridge of land across what is now the Bering Strait. No one knows just when the Indians began to cross that bridge. We do know that the time was thousands of years before Europeans found this land.

Indians were already here when some Chinese came to visit California about 500 B.C. Viking fishermen found Indians on the Atlantic coast between the years 900 and 1000. Some five hundred years later, Columbus went looking for India and found North America instead. Thinking the island he had reached in the Caribbean was off the coast of India, Columbus called its people Indians. They are still called Indians, the name they were given by mistake.

At the time of the Spanish explorers, there were about a million Indians living north of Mexico. In California alone there were some fifty tribes. One of these, the Chumash, lived along the coast from San Luis Obispo south. They had plenty of food. The weather was kind. The Chumash lived very peacefully.

Then the Spanish missionaries came along. The missionaries tried to make the Chumash change their very satisfactory way of life. To the Chumash it seemed that life at the missions would not be worth living. Some of them ran away. The rest simply stopped raising families. Within a few years, the free and peaceful Chumash had become a vanished tribe.

"Chumash Boy" is a story of the happier days. It is the story of a boy who braved many dangers—and who saw Cabrillo come to California in 1542.

CONTENTS

Chumash Boy

I

Chumash Boy sat in the shadow of the rock, waiting. He had planned his escape well. It was almost time for him to start.

Moonlight lay across the water. The tide was coming in. The boy must wait only a little longer. Behind him, the village was quiet. Smoke rose from a dying fire. A guard sat beside the fire.

"The guard will soon be sleepy," thought Chumash Boy.

The young Indian had been hiding beside the rock for a long time. He had hardly dared to move or breathe. Closer and closer came the water. Now there was only a tiny strip of sand between the water and his hiding place.

Somewhere a dog barked, and another joined in. Chumash Boy looked at the man by the fire. He was asleep. The noise had not wakened him.

It was now or never! The boy slipped from his hiding place. His nets and harpoon were already in his boat. He quickly found the other things he had hidden for his trip. Water, tools, weapons, his robe—all were in his boat. He pushed the boat quietly across the sand. His heart was beating fast.

With one last push, the boat was free. Chumash Boy had no time to waste now. He paddled hard. He did not look back until he was far out on the water.

The boy saw dots of light all along the shore. They were the fires of the Chumash villages that lined the ocean. There, near the river, was the village the boy had just left. It was Shuku, his home.

Chumash Boy saw the fires of Kolok far away. Enemies of his family lived there. Many moons ago, they had come to his village in the night. They had set fire to his father's house. The fire had burned everything his family owned.

Many of his family had been lost in the fire. Chumash Boy and his father had lived, but the boy had been badly burned.

The boy and his father had been saved because they were not in their house. Each night the Chumash men and older boys went to the sweat house to smoke and talk. They often slept there, too.

The next day the father had set off for Kolok. But he had never reached his enemies' village. And he had never come back.

Chumash Boy had lived in his uncle's house since that night. His uncle was lazy and evil. He was not a kind man.

The chiefs of Shuku and Kolok had met after the fire. They had decided that the Kolok Indians must pay for what had been burned. The enemies had given many skins, baskets, and strings of shells to Chumash Boy. But his evil uncle had taken all of them. With his father gone, there was no one to get them back for the boy.

"You are too young for these things," the uncle had said. "I will keep them for you."

But the boy had known that his uncle was lying. He had known that his uncle would never give the things to him.

The uncle had also said many things that were not true about Chumash Boy's father. "He did not try to go to Kolok," the uncle had said. "Your father was afraid to fight his enemies. He ran away. He brought shame on our family."

Chumash Boy looked up at the bright stars. "The rest of my family are star people now," he thought. "Someday I will find out what happened to my father. Then I will return and tell my people the truth."

The paddle lay across the boy's knees. Both ends of the paddle were flat and wide. The young Indian held the paddle tightly. It had belonged to his father.

"My father was strong and wise and brave. He did not run away," the boy said to himself. He dipped the paddle into the water, first on one side of the boat, then on the other. The little boat shot forward.

The moon was bright. Across the water, Chumash Boy could see the dark shape of an island. He pushed on. The waves slapped hard against his boat.

He must not let the current carry him too far south. There was one island he must miss. Its people were not Chumash Indians. They spoke a strange tongue and had strange ways. They built their huts of skins and the bones of whales. The people on this island guarded their fishing waters day and night. Any Chumash found in those waters would be killed.

Chumash Boy fought the current with all his might. His arms and back hurt. At last he could fight no longer. He laid the paddle across his knees.

He prayed, "Oh, Spirit of my Father, carry me to a safe place."

Then the boy's head dropped. His eyes closed. The water lapped softly against his boat. He listened for a time and thought, "Surely, I will not drift far." He was soon asleep.

The cry of sea birds wakened the runaway boy. He heard the roar of waves—just in time! His boat was in danger of being thrown against the rocks! He paddled hard. At last he moved his boat away from the rocks and into a small bay.

Chumash Boy jumped into the water. He quickly pulled his boat up onto the sand. But when he looked about him, his heart sank. The current had taken him to the wrong island.

There were no villages on this island. It was very small. It was covered with brush. Chumash Boy knew that fishermen sometimes camped here. But he seemed to be alone on the island now.

The boy looked at the many birds flying high in the air. "There will be plenty of eggs and fish to eat here," he thought. "But what about water?" His water basket was almost empty. He must find more water soon.

An old trail led up from the shore. There was a chance that it led to a spring. The boy had to find out. He climbed the trail. Loose rocks rolled down the hill behind him.

Chumash Boy had not gone far when he found a small hut. There were bones and fish heads everywhere. He saw what was left of a fire. "Some fishermen must have left this," he said to himself. With his foot, he felt the gray ashes.

The ashes were still warm! Someone was on the island now. Was it a fisherman? Or was it an outlaw from one of the villages?

The boy looked at the ground carefully. He saw the print of a man's foot. If an outlaw were on the island, the young Indian would certainly be in danger.

He thought of his boat on the beach. Turning, he ran back over the rocks. At one place he fell. At that very moment, a big rock sailed over his head. If he had not fallen, it would have hit him.

At last Chumash Boy reached the beach. He quickly shoved his boat into the water. With a running jump, he was in it. He paddled for his life. All at once, he heard a noise. Turning, he saw an arrow stuck in the side of his boat.

The boy did not stop paddling until he felt that he was safe again. Then he rested a moment. He took a long drink from his nearly empty water basket. The basket was one his grandmother had made long ago. It was woven of grasses. Inside, it was covered with tar to make it watertight.

Chumash Boy looked over the other things in his boat. He had brought only what he would need to keep himself alive. There was a robe made of rabbitskins. It would keep him warm at night. Like the other boys of his tribe, he wore no clothing in summer. But he rubbed mud on his arms and legs when it was cold. And he sometimes wore a fur robe in the winter.

The cooking basket that Chumash Boy had brought along was also lined with tar. He had a large carrying basket with him, too. But his tools were very few. He carried his fire sticks in a net wound around his waist. The knife his father had made for him was stuck in his hair. He was especially proud of this knife. Its handle was made of polished wood. Its blade was a hard piece of stone. He sharpened the blade with flint.

Chumash Boy also had a throwing stick in his boat. With this, he could kill rabbits and other small animals. Although he had brought along only a few pine nuts to eat, he had his fine harpoon with him. Perhaps he might even kill a sea lion with it.

Tired though he was, the boy knew that he had been resting long enough. His first job was to catch some fish. It was many hours since he had eaten.

From a small bag, Chumash Boy took some ground cactus leaves. He put the ground leaves into the water for bait. Then he threw out his net and waited. As he waited, he thought of his fine boat. It took a long time to make such a boat.

The boy's people had gone far up the river to the mountain. The men had hunted through the thick forest for fallen trees. They had split the fallen logs into planks and had carried the rough boards down to the village. They had scraped the planks smooth with sharp shells, and had made holes in them. Putting strips of leather through the holes, they had then tied the planks together. Finally they had filled every crack and hole with hot tar. As soon as the tar was dry, the boat was ready.

Proud of his boat, Chumash Boy said to himself, "My people make the best boats of all."

He was right. The Chumash people made better boats than any of the other Indians who lived in California.

3

The sun was low in the sky. Chumash Boy ate two of the smaller fish he had caught. He put the other four into his net and closed it. Then he put the net behind his boat to drag along in the water. The boy's mouth was dry, but all his drinking water was gone.

Chumash Boy knew that he must get to the big island before night came. He knew of a village there, called Nimalala. He was sure of a welcome there. Nimalala men had often come to Shuku to trade.

The boy stood up in his boat, looking at the shore. Suddenly, the boat rocked so hard that it nearly upset. Chumash Boy was thrown on his back. His paddle flew out of his hand. Crying with pain, he crawled to the back of the boat. He looked over the edge.

A few bits of net were left. But his four precious fish were gone!

Chumash Boy was angry. He hit his fist against the boat. Then he saw the shark. Its big, wet body and strong teeth shone in the sun. After eating, the boy had thrown the fish heads over the side of his boat. The blood had brought the shark. Chumash Boy thought fast. His paddle was drifting away. He could not swim after it. The shark would kill him. Without the paddle, he would be lost!

There was only one thing to do. The boy grabbed his harpoon. With a great jab, he drove it into the shark's throat. The big fish rolled over. Knife in hand, Chumash Boy dived from the boat. He swam after his paddle.

The shark was fighting for its life. Chumash Boy reached the boat with his paddle. He pulled himself over the side.

The shark was tired. Before long, it was floating, belly up and quite still. Chumash Boy paddled up beside it. This time he would not lose his catch!

The boy tugged and pulled until the wet body was in his boat. The shark was nearly as long as he was.

He dipped the paddle into the dark water and made for the shore. Some children came out to meet him. Their eyes were wide when they saw the shark.

"Your chief was my father's friend," Chumash Boy told them. "Take me to him."

The chief was tall and strong. His robe came down to his feet. It was made of beautiful feathers. The chief looked kindly at Chumash Boy. He saw the boy's many burns. He saw that the boy's hair was cut short. This was the Indian sign that there had been a death in the family.

The chief called to his wife, "Bring water and food." Then he said to Chumash Boy, "Come, my son. You are welcome here."

Chumash Boy entered the chief's house. The chief was the richest man in the village. Even so, his house was poorer than the houses on the mainland. Chumash Boy saw sleeping mats on the floor. At home, his people slept on raised beds.

"I have killed a shark," the boy said. "It is in my boat. You will find acorn meal there, too." He knew that these people had little to eat but fish. He was glad that he had brought the shark and the acorn meal to them.

The chief smiled, then said, "But you must rest now. I will send someone for the things in your boat."

When Chumash Boy had eaten, he told the chief about his family. Then he added in a low voice, "It is said that my father ran away. You knew my father, oh, Chief. Do you believe that?"

"I do not," answered the chief. "I knew your father well." Then he added in a cold voice, "And—I know your uncle!"

Chumash Boy looked into the old man's eyes. Could it be that the chief knew more than he was telling?

Whatever it was, the old man was not yet ready to say more. "If you are rested enough, tell me of your escape," he said to Chumash Boy.

"I planned for many days to leave Shuku," the boy began. "A little at a time, I gathered the things I would need for my trip. I hid them away. But my uncle kept watching my father's boat.

"When the time came to gather the pine nuts and acorns, the people of my village went to the mountain. Only the old men and women stayed behind. My uncle wanted to stay, too. But our chief made him go.

"I went with them. But on the fourth day of the harvest, I slipped away. I ran back to our village. It was dark when I reached the river. I waited until the old people of the village were asleep. Then I started across the water."

Then Chumash Boy told the chief what had happened to him on the island. He told of his fight with the shark. The chief sat quietly for a time. Then he said, "It is well that you left Shuku. There is much that I must tell you. But it can wait until morning. Sleep now, my son."

4

Chumash Boy smelled steaming mush. The chief's wife was cooking breakfast. She put hot stones into the cooking basket with some water and acorn meal. Then she added a few pieces of fish. The mush was soon cooked. The woman took the stones out of the basket and left the mush to cool.

After breakfast, the Chief spoke to Chumash Boy. "You must leave here, my son. Your uncle will notice that the boat is gone. He will know that you left by water. He knows that

9

I am your father's friend. He may come here to look for you."

"But why should he come to look for me?" the boy asked. "He hates me. Why would he want to take me back to Shuku?"

"Do not forget that your uncle had much to gain by your father's death," the chief said. "You will soon be a man. Then you will ask for what is rightly yours."

"But I won't do that," Chumash Boy cried. "I don't want anything from my uncle. And I don't want to live in my uncle's house."

"He is a man without honor," the chief said. "He lives with fear. If he finds you, you will never get home alive."

The boy was quiet. Could it be that his uncle was a truly evil man?

"Listen. I was told this story," the chief said. "A trading party came to the sea from a village beyond the mountain. On the way home, they found a dying man on the trail. There was a knife wound in his back. The men carried him across the mountain to their village.

"The daughter of their chief took pity on the wounded man. She watched over him for many moons. The man began to get better.

"The man soon grew strong and well. But he had forgotten his name, and where he came from."

Chumash Boy jumped to his feet. "Oh, Chief, that man was my father! I feel sure he was."

"Wait, my son," answered the chief. "We cannot be sure of that yet. But I was told this, too. The man was found on the trail that leads to Kolok. His hair was cut close to his head—the sign of a death in the family."

The boy's eyes burned. "Who told you this?" he asked.

"A messenger from Tukan."

Chumash Boy thought quickly. Tukan was a village on a small island far to the north of Nimalala. It would take many, many hours of paddling to get to Tukan.

"I must leave at once," he said. "I must talk to the messenger from Tukan."

The chief nodded. "Your boat is ready. You will find food for the trip and a new net in it. My friends at Tukan will help you."

"I cannot find words to thank you, oh, Chief," said Chumash Boy. "I go now."

"Go," the old man said. This was the Indian way of saying good-by.

Chumash Boy set off. He paddled out into the water and stayed far from shore. The sky was clear, but the water was rough.

"The time of strong winds and high waters will be coming soon," he thought.

Later that day, Chumash Boy saw a great whale. It was rolling and diving. The boy was glad when it turned and swam away. No Indian would try to kill a great whale. But one of the huge beasts sometimes swam into shallow water and died there. Then the Indians used its bones to make tools.

Chumash Boy paddled all night long. He could not lose time sleeping. Black clouds sailed across the moon. The wind rose. Then he heard the roll of thunder. The boy fought the storm all night. But the sky was clear again when morning came. At last he could see the island where Tukan was. He knew that his journey was almost over.

In the harbor at last, Chumash Boy saw a strange sight—two ships with tall, white wings. The boy moved closer. Was this a war party from some faraway tribe? Would he find the messenger at Tukan dead or alive? His heart beat fast as he paddled for the shore.

5

Chumash Boy ran through Tukan. All the Indians there were busy. If they were making ready for war, he saw no signs of it. At last he found the chief's house.

The chief spoke to the boy kindly. "Good. You have come in time for our feast. We have other visitors, too."

"I saw the tall boats," said Chumash Boy.

"These men come from far away," the chief told him. "They speak a strange tongue. They have strange ways. But they are friendly."

Then the chief smiled. "That is enough about the men for now," he said. "I know that you want news of your father."

"Yes, yes," the boy cried.

A young Indian entered the chief's house. He was the messenger Chumash Boy was seeking. He told Chumash Boy the same story that the first chief had told him.

"Take me to the village beyond the mountain," begged Chumash Boy.

"Let me see my father. Then perhaps he will remember."

The chief shook his head. "Your uncle might follow. Your father's life would be in danger. No, you must stay here. We have a better plan."

The messenger said, "I will go to your father. I will bring him to Nimalala. Later, you will meet us there. The chief will help you and your father get back to Shuku."

Chumash Boy did not want to stay behind. But he knew that this plan was safer. He pulled the knife from his hair.

"Take this with you," he said. "My father made it. When he sees it, he may remember."

The messenger took the knife. "I go now," he said.

"Go," spoke the chief.

Chumash Boy walked to the beach with the messenger. "You risk much for me," the boy said.

"It is nothing," said the young Indian. "You would do the same for me."

The messenger's boat was soon out on the black water and out of sight. The boy turned, his heart filled with shame.

"I am a coward," he said to himself. "I ran away from home. I would not fight for what was mine. I did no evil. But I let another man do evil. That is just as wrong."

But the boy's mind was made up now. He would go back to Shuku. He would see to it that wrong was made right. As he went back over the trail to Tukan, he felt strong and good inside.

The singing and dancing at Tukan lasted far into the night. The strange men came to the feast. They brought gifts of beads and cloth for all the Indians.

Many of the white men were weak and sick. Their leader had hurt his arm. Chumash Boy noticed that they did not eat any of the Indians' raw fish. He saw their strange knives. They were not made of wood or stone or shell. The blades were hard and bright.

"I do not know why they came here," Chumash Boy said to himself. "But it is a sign from the Spirits. I feel it in my heart. My people have

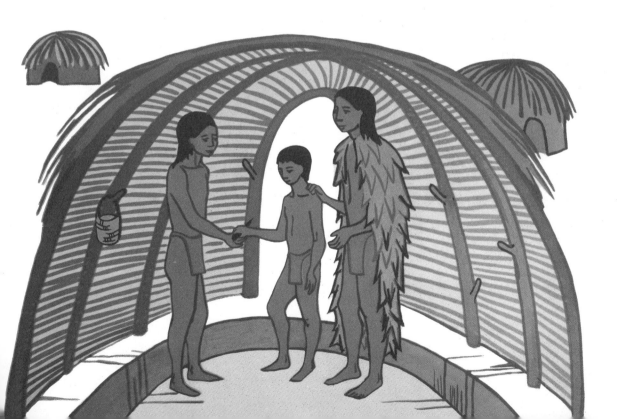

kept the land as it was in the beginning. But these men—they will bring a change."

When the storm was over, it was time for the strange men to leave. Chumash Boy helped carry wood and water to their ships. At last they set off across the water. The tall, white wings of their ships filled with wind. They were soon out of sight.

Chumash Boy thought of the strange men many times. They had been kind and friendly. But still he was uneasy.

The days passed slowly. Chumash Boy waited for the messenger.

As he waited, Chumash Boy did what he could to help his friends in Tukan. He helped to build a house. Long poles were placed in a circle. They were tied together at the top.

Grass mats were tied onto the frame. The women dug a wide pit in the middle of the house. They carried the dirt outside and put it against the walls. Then they smoothed the floor. The house had two doors and a smoke hole at the top. There was a shelf of earth all around the inside.

When the house was finished, a family moved into their new home. They held a feast. All the Indians in the village came. They ran races and played games. They sang and danced far into the night.

Chumash Boy waited and waited for the messenger to come back. But there was still no word of his father. Then one day, he at last heard a shout from the beach. He ran down the trail to the water's edge. His heart was beating fast.

When Chumash Boy looked out over the bay, his heart sank. He did not see the messenger's boat. Instead, he saw the tall, white wings again.

"Why do the white men come back?" Chumash Boy asked himself.

He soon found out. Their ships needed to be repaired. And their leader was very sick. The brave man was dying.

The people of Tukan were glad to help the white men. Once again, they took wood and water to the white men's ships. They helped to repair them. An Indian law said that every Indian must care for all those in need of help.

The moon of strong winds was almost over. Then one day, a party of white men came from their ships. Their faces were sad. They carried the body of their leader. They made a grave for him on the island and marked it with a cross. Chumash Boy could not read the words on the wooden cross. They would have told him that the dead leader was Juan Rodríguez Cabrillo. Soon afterward, the tall ships sailed away.

One day the chief called for Chumash Boy. "I have news for you," the old man said. "You must go now. Your father is at Nimalala."

Chumash Boy fell on his knees before the chief. "I do not know how to thank you," he said.

"You are always welcome here, my son. Remember that, but go now," the chief told him.

Chumash Boy said good-by to his friends. He quickly made his boat ready. As he left the bay, he looked back at the wooden cross. He thought of the white men, with their strong ships and strange tools.

"They have left their mark upon our land," he said to himself. "One day they will come again. What will become of my people?"

But these thoughts were soon forgotten. His heart filled with joy as the boat neared Nimalala. For the messenger stood by the water. Beside him stood another man, tall and strong. He smiled and held out his arms to Chumash Boy.

The boy dropped his paddle and jumped from the boat. "Father," he cried. "You do remember me!"

His father said, "For many moons I lived in shadow, my son. Then a knife was placed in my hand. The shadows lifted and I cried out for joy."

"It is true," said the messenger.

"Remembering brought pain as well as joy," his father went on. "I saw the fire, as if in a dream. I saw my brother hiding in the smoke. When he turned, I saw he had two faces. We must go back to Shuku, my son. Our people must know of the evil in our village."

The chief of Nimalala sent a messenger to Shuku. He was to say only that a trading party was coming from the island.

A few days later, the party set out. There were many boats and many men in the party. Chumash Boy and his father were among them.

The boy said to his father, "I want to see Uncle's face when he finds that you are alive."

The boy's father smiled and said, "It will not be long now. Look! The people of Shuku are waiting by the water to welcome us."

Chumash Boy and his father jumped from their boat. Together, they walked up behind the uncle. The father placed a hand on the uncle's arm. The evil man turned. His eyes grew wide.

"Brother, are you not happy to see me?" asked the father.

The evil man could not speak. He tried to pull away, but his brother held on to his arm.

"Come," said Chumash Boy's father. "Let us find our chief. We have much to tell him."

The chief looked first at Chumash Boy and then at his father.

"How is this?" he asked. "We thought that you were dead these many moons."

"Ask this one," the father said in a cold voice. He threw his brother to the ground. The man lay there, shaking with fear.

The boy's father spoke to the chief. "Many moons ago, I set off for our enemies' village. On the way, some-one stuck a knife into my back. He left me, thinking that I was dead. It was this man—my own brother.

"I was found by a trading party," Chumash Boy's father went on. "They took me to their village, where I stayed for many moons. The people of Nimalala and Tukan helped my son to find me."

The chief raised his hand. "Wait," he said, turning to the father. "Do you have proof that the man who struck you was your brother?"

The father held out a bone ring.

"I made this for my brother when we were boys," he said. "He always wore it. But it slipped from his hand when he tried to kill me."

The uncle began to crawl away, looking at the ring. The other Indians began to whisper to one another. Chumash Boy knew that all of them believed what his father had said.

The chief said angrily to the uncle, "You bring shame on your family, and on our village. Go at once! Never return to Shuku!"

Then the chief turned to Chumash Boy and his father. "Welcome home," he said. "Tomorrow we'll start work on your new house. But tonight—we shall feast and dance!"

The boy walked proudly beside his father up the trail. At last his long journey was ended.

HOW WELL DO YOU REMEMBER THE STORY?

Number your paper from 1 to 20. After each number put T *if the sentence is true or* N *if the sentence is not true.*

1. Chumash Boy waited until the sun came up before he tried to escape from Shuku.
2. Enemies from Kolok had burned his father's house.
3. The chiefs of the two villages had decided that the Kolok Indians did not have to pay for what was burned.
4. Chumash Boy was quite sure that his uncle was telling lies about his father.
5. When Chumash Boy landed on the first small island, he began to look for eggs.
6. The boy had nothing but a bag of ground cactus leaves to eat when he was hungry.
7. His boat was made of planks tied together with strips of leather.
8. Many of the California Indians made better boats than the Chumash people.
9. Chumash Boy caught some small fish, but the birds ate them all.
10. The boy had to kill the shark so he could get his paddle back again.
11. The chief at Nimalala had been the enemy of Chumash Boy's father.
12. The island Indians slept on mats on the floor.
13. The mainland Indians and the island Indians did not trade with one another.
14. Tukan was a village on the same island as Nimalala.
15. The ships that Chumash Boy saw at Tukan brought strangers from far away.
16. A messenger was sent from Tukan to the village where Chumash Boy's father was believed to be.
17. The white men's leader was named Juan Rodríguez Cabrillo.
18. A messenger brought word that Chumash Boy's uncle was waiting at Nimalala.

19. The uncle was happy to see that Chumash Boy and his father were safe.
20. The chief sent the uncle away from the village.

Choose the right ending for each of the sentences below. Write each sentence on your paper.

1. Nets and harpoons were used for (hunting, fishing, cooking).
2. Ground cactus leaves were used for (bait, clothing, polishing wood).
3. Baskets covered with tar were used for (rabbits, pine nuts, water).
4. Fire sticks were fastened around the waist in a (net, basket, pot).
5. Throwing sticks were used for (games, hunting, dancing).
6. Knife blades were made of (wood, flint, stone).
7. Chumash boats were made of (grass, leather, planks).
8. Houses were made of (stone and mud, leather and planks, poles and grass).
9. Food was carried in (glass jars, baskets, paper sacks).

From the sentences below, choose those which are true and write them on your paper.

1. Indian women slept in the sweat houses with their paddles.
2. Some Indians cut their hair short after a death in the family.
3. Giving help to strangers was against Indian law.
4. Indians had to pay when they broke laws.
5. The Indians went to the mountains to gather bones.

PEOPLE OF THE SHADOWED PAST

archaeologist (ar·kē·ol′o·jist), *n.* A person who studies the past by finding and studying everyday things that long-ago people left behind them.

prehistoric (prē′his·tor′ik), *adj.* A word used to describe the time before history was written; *pre*history means *before* history.

totem (tō′tem), *n.* A sign or symbol, like a certain plant, animal, or thing, that an Indian family took as its own.

potlatch (pot′lach′), *n.* This comes from a Chinook Indian word meaning *giving* or *gift*; a big party, usually given in the winter, at which the Indians gave each other gifts.

fertilize (fur′ti·līz), *v.* To put something into soil to make it rich so that better crops can be grown in it.

missionaries (mish′un·air′iz), *n.* Men sent from one country to try to get people in another country to follow the beliefs of the first country.

explorer (eks·plōr′er), *n.* A person who travels to new lands and tries to find out all about them.

frontier (frun·tēr′), *n.* Used here to mean the land between the settled and the not yet settled parts of a country.

tribe (trīb), *n.* A word used here to describe a group of Indians who lived in the same part of the country and spoke the same language.

prey (prā), *n.* A person or animal that falls under the power of another.

reservation (rez′er·vā′shun), *n.* A large piece of land that is supposed to be kept for some certain use.

minority (mi·nor′i·ti), *n.* A group that is smaller in number than other groups.

heritage (her′i·tij), *n.* That which comes down to people from the members of their group who lived before them.

AMERICA'S FIRST FAMILIES

Archaeologists are seeking answers to many questions about man's shadowed past. How did man live a half million years ago? In what ways was he different from us? How have the changes come about?

Some of the answers have been found in long-buried camps and villages. Bits of bone, clay, and stone discovered in such places tell part of the story. Not long ago a very old cooking pit was discovered on one of the islands where the Chumash lived. In the pit were the bones of a mammoth —a prehistoric animal that looked something like an elephant. The bones found in the pit had been pulled apart. It looked as though the meat had been cooked and eaten. One of America's earliest families had enjoyed that meal about 29,650 years ago!

It must have been a family of Indians. The Indians were America's first families.

CHINESE INDIANS?

Some other interesting things have come to light about the Indian group to which Chumash Boy belonged. Early Spanish writers told of finding bits of dishes and of metal on Chumash shores. They thought the bits and pieces must have come from China. Chinese history does record that people from that country visited our part of the world some 2500 years ago.

For this or some other reason, the Spanish sometimes called the Chumash "the little Chinamen of California." It was noted that the Chumash had lighter skin than other Indians. Their homes and boats were large and well built. Their tools and other belongings, though simple, were beautifully made.

In some Chumash villages, there were as many as a hundred houses. Some were big enough to hold fifty people. Inside each house were raised beds made of poles and grass mats. Each bed had a blanket made out of thin strips of fur or animal hide.

As to most present-day Americans, wealth was important to the Chumash. The more riches a man had, the more important his place in the group. Chumash riches were counted in terms of shell money, threaded on strings of hide. Boats, tools, and other belongings were also signs of wealth. How rich a Chumash grew may have depended on how good a trader he was. The Chumash seem to have traded with faraway Indians as well as with their neighbors.

Food is always the first need of all peoples. The Indians had to spend nearly all their time gathering and fixing things to eat. The Chumash used sticks for digging roots and insects out of the ground. To make the sticks heavier, and so easier to use, stone rings were slipped over them. Many of those early digging tools have been found.

From the thickly wooded hills, the Chumash gathered acorns, pine nuts, and wild berries. They also ate frogs, insects, worms, and grasshoppers. None of these things were eaten just as they were found. They had to be carefully prepared. Some things were roasted or sun-dried. Others were ground to a powder or pounded.

The Chumash had good stones for grinding food. Chumash grinding stones were traded far and wide. So were their fine baskets, many of them beautifully decorated. The plain ones may have been used for carrying food. The fancy ones may have been for carrying gifts or offerings to the gods. If a basket was to be used to carry water, it was lined with tar.

Beautiful stone bowls were also made and traded by the Chumash. Those that have been found show no signs of hard wear. This may mean that they were used for drinking, not for cooking.

Hunting and fishing, of course, were important ways of getting food. Common Chumash hunting weapons were stone knives, clubs, throwing sticks, bows and arrows. The Chumash made these things for their own use and for trading.

There were lots of fish where most of the Chumash lived. The men were good fishermen and good boat-builders. The Chumash boats were made from planks fastened together with animal hides. The same tar that was used to line baskets was used in boat-building. It was heated and poured into the holes where the pieces of hide went through the planks. When the tar cooled, the boat was watertight. A Chumash boat was worth a lot of shell money.

CHUMASH CUSTOMS

The Chumash had some mountain caves. We are still trying to find out what they were used for. Whatever their use, the walls of the caves are covered with strange and beautiful paintings. Some are paintings of men or animals. Others seem to be paintings of gods. Still others show the sun and stars.

Also found in the caves were bowls, baskets, charm stones and belongings of every sort. The people of certain Pacific islands used secret caves as storing places for treasured family belongings. Perhaps the caves in the Santa Barbara mountains served the Chumash people in this way.

We know that the caves were not used as burying grounds. The Chumash buried their dead in graves. Each grave was marked with a tall, painted pole. If the dead person was a woman, a basket was hung from the pole. If the grave was a man's, his long hair was cut and some of it was fastened to the pole.

When a Chumash died, many of his treasured belongings were buried with him. Some of their laws showed that belongings were important to the Chumash. If one person stole from another, the thief had to pay a fine. Anyone who did any kind of harm to another had to pay a fine. Most of the time the fines were paid in shell money.

An Indian who wished to marry had to pay the girl's family. Different kinds of goods, as well as shell money, made up the payment.

Women were held in high honor by the Chumash. It was the Chumash who greeted Cabrillo when he came to California. An old woman, chief of a dozen villages, made him welcome. She had food and water sent to his ship. Being a true Chumash, she also arranged for some trading between her people and Cabrillo's.

Cabrillo and his men made friends with the Chumash. Stories of the kind white strangers were passed along from father to son in Chumash families. It was not until more than two hundred years later that the Chumash began to fear white men. That was when white men began to arrive in great numbers. That was when white men began to take over the land that had belonged to the Indians. Worst of all, many of the white strangers seemed to look down on the Chumash. This was a bitter blow to the proud people who had ruled their land in their own way for so many hundreds of years.

Little by little, the Chumash began to feel that life was no longer worth living. They could not, or would not, change with the changing world. They did not want to bring children into such a world. Families became smaller and smaller. At last there were no Chumash Indians left.

A GLANCE AT OTHER INDIANS

The kind of life led by any group of Indians depended a great deal on where they were living. The weather, the soil, and the plant and animal life all had much to do with it.

Some of the Plains Indians were always hunters. Many of them lived in huts made out of earth and sod. Later, after the Spanish brought horses to North America, the Plains Indians changed their ways. No longer did they need to hunt within a few miles of their huts. With horses, they could follow buffalo and other game to faraway hunting grounds. So—they changed their form of housing. Instead of huts, they used tents. They could take the tents with them no matter where they went.

Along the Pacific coast, the men were often fishermen. The women gathered seeds and roots and berries. Some of the Indians, like the Chumash, made good boats. Some built strong wooden houses.

Many pieces of fine wood carving have been found in the remains of Indian villages. Indians in the Northwest carved stories into their tall totem poles. The stories were told at great feasts, called potlatches. Everyone gave gifts to everyone else at those Indian parties. Parties like them are still given, and not only by Indians, in the Pacific Northwest.

Most of the Indians in the Southwest raised some crops. Their villages, called pueblos, were made up of apartment-like dwellings cut into the sides of cliffs. Some of these early apartment houses can still be seen today.

In the wooded lands of eastern America, and along the banks of the Colorado in the West, the Indians often farmed. Potatoes, pumpkins, watermelons, and rice were Indian crops. Some Indians learned to use sap from maple trees. Others, in South America, found uses for cocoa beans. Still others made many kinds of medicine from plants.

You have heard that the Pilgrim fathers learned about corn from the Indians. The Indians, so the story goes, had harvested their corn and stored it for the winter. A party of Pilgrims found it and took it for themselves. It was the first time they had ever tasted corn, and they liked it. The Indians must have been kind, forgiving people. Instead of being angry about the missing corn, they showed the Pilgrims how to raise their own. They even showed their new neighbors how to fertilize the soil with dead fish.

WHITE MAN AGAINST INDIAN

Indians generally welcomed with kindness the first white men to come to their great wild land. But their kindness was ill repaid. The white man has little to be proud of in his record of dealing with the Indians.

In the West, soldiers, missionaries, hunters, and trappers followed after Cabrillo. There were other explorers, too, less kindly than Cabrillo and his men. Indians like the Chumash had lived peaceful lives. They did not know how to protect themselves or their lands against the white man.

In the East and the Southeast and the Southwest, other white men moved against the Indian. The sad story of the Chumash found echoes in many parts of the country. The settlement of the frontier became largely a matter of conquering the Indians.

The white man wanted land. The land belonged to the Indian tribes. Not surprisingly, the Indians were not always willing to give up their tribal lands. But soon there were more white men than Indians in the country. The white men used all kinds of means to get the land they wanted. Sometimes the Indians were driven away by force. Sometimes they were tricked by false promises. Sometimes the white men started fights between different groups of Indians.

Groups that did not trust one another or work together were easier prey for the white men.

The white man's government made promises to the Indian governments. The eastern Indians agreed to move west to large pieces of land called reservations. The white man's government promised that those lands would belong to the Indians from then on. Other promises were made, too. The Indians were promised food, clothing, and schooling for their children. In some cases they were told they would never have to pay taxes.

FORGOTTEN PROMISES

Little by little, all the eastern groups of Indians were pushed toward the west. Most eastern Indians were forced to move west of the Mississippi. The land set aside for Indian use was almost always land that the white man did not want. Later it was found that many of the Indian lands were valuable. Some were found to have rich stores of oil or metals. Others were wanted as grazing lands by the white owners of sheep and cattle.

One after another, the promises made to the Indians were broken. It was said that the Indians had no real right to certain pieces of land. Some ninety million acres were taken back from them. This is one of the reasons so many Indians are poor today.

Other promises were badly kept. Sometimes the food sent to Indians was not fit to eat. The schooling given them has always been very poor. In some places, even today, children cannot go to school because they do not have the clothes they need.

The proud Navajos, once the lords of the whole Southwest, are better off than most Indians. Yet most of the men and women on the Navajo lands cannot read or write.

Thousands of their children are getting no schooling either. Some of the children who do go to school are not much better off. They are often taught as though they were going to live ordinary American lives away from their Indian lands. Yet those who leave the reservation often find that this is not the case. They find that their schooling has robbed them of some of their proud sense of belonging to a great tribe. But they have been given nothing to take its place.

Indians find it hard to get jobs. They find it hard to get proper housing. All too often, in the outside world, they are made to feel like second-class citizens. This is hard to take. After all, Indians are the only true Americans among us!

NORTH AMERICAN INDIANS TODAY

Many well-meaning people today are trying to make up for the way the white man has treated Indians. Nothing can be done, of course, to bring back the Chumash or other groups that were destroyed. Much can be done, however, for the Indians now alive. First of all, they must be given their rights as American citizens.

Some 600,000 Indians live in this, their country. About 308,000 of them live on reservations. There are about a hundred of these big pieces of land. Most of them are pockets of poverty. The Indians who live on them have not been given all the rights that other Americans enjoy.

WHAT ARE THE PROBLEMS?

Not until 1924 were Indians given the right to vote. Even now, in some places, they cannot vote for state officers. In other places, they cannot take cases to court as other citizens do. Some kinds of government aid given to other Americans are kept from the Indians. Thousands of Indians fought bravely in World War II. Other Americans, who fought side by side with them, were given certain "G.I." aids when they went home. But there were many Indians, just as deserving, who could not get such aids.

Many Indians have left the Indian lands. Some have gone into business in the outside world. Others have become doctors, teachers, artists, or government workers. One group of Mohawks in New York are famous as steel workers.

Most of the Indians living "on the outside" are making a living. Still, they do not have an easy time. They have the same kinds of trouble that other minority groups have. They have a few of their own, besides. As a group, Indians have lower incomes than any other Americans. Many suffer from poor health. Some never get used to living in crowded cities instead of on open land.

But the open land that is left to them is mostly very poor land indeed. The soil is poor. There is not enough water in most places. It is a hopeless task to try to make a good living from the land.

Some people think the thing to do is get all Indians to leave the Indian lands. Others, including many Indians, do not agree. Many people who study the subject feel that the proud Indian heritage should be saved. Tribal pride is one of the few things the Indian has left. Must he give it up and become "lost" in the swift stream of American life, as people from other countries have? Or can he be treated as a first-class citizen even though he stays on Indian lands, following age-old Indian ways?

Other people point out that many of the Indian ways are already lost. The young men and women do not want to learn the old, old arts. They want to live like other present-day Americans.

SUSC Curriculum Library

One promising sign is that Indian groups have begun to speak their minds. The National Congress of American Indians made this statement a few years ago:

"... the Indians ask for assistance, technical and financial ... to regain in the America of the space age some measure of the adjustment they enjoyed as the original possessors of their native land."

The National Indian Youth Council is made up of young men of the tribes. Its president said:

"Indians need help in developing resources on their own reservations ... their ancestral homes ... which they want to be allowed to live on peacefully. In short, they want 'home rule.' They don't want Congress treating them like children."

It is true that Congress and the Bureau of Indian Affairs have seemed to treat Indians like children. Indians living on Indian lands are not free to do very many things without asking the government first. They cannot even start a business. Often, of course, the government is willing to let them go into business. But if they do start a business, the money they make goes to the government. The government is supposed to keep it in trust, giving it back as needed. Not even that money can be spent by the group unless the government is willing.

Long before there were any white men here, Indians were running their own lives. They had to decide such things as how best to get food for large groups of people. They set up their own law and government. Rules had to be made about rights to land. The Indians did all these things and did them well. They were careful not to waste the riches of the land. They tried to make sure that every person in a group was treated fairly.

But today, the white man's government is making most of the rules. For every eighteen Indians in the United States, the Bureau of Indian Affairs has one worker on its rolls. Many Indians think they could do without so many people to look after them. They feel that the money paid to those people could be put to better use.

WHAT SHOULD BE DONE?

Many people feel that the government should, first of all, give Indians the best possible schooling. Head Start classes have been opened on some Indian lands. Most Indian leaders want more such classes. They want better grade schools and high schools. They want colleges to be opened on the largest reservations. Most of all, they want Indians to be trained with their way of life in mind. Such training can be given only by people who really understand Indians. They need to understand how Indians feel about land and time and nature. They also need to know what life is like in America's mainstream.

Well-schooled Indians, when there are enough of them, can do much to make life on Indian lands a true part of the American Way. Indians who have been to good schools will also be able to do more to help improve American life "on the outside."

On or off their own lands, Indians have a right to good housing. They have a right to equal chances for jobs. Their right to go to court must be the same as other people's. All these rights must be given. Once given, they must be protected.

In other words, Indians must be treated as truly first-class citizens. Then they can decide for themselves the best road for them to follow in American life. Whatever road they choose is likely to be the right one.

TO TALK ABOUT IN CLASS

1. What do you think may have happened to the land bridge that once crossed the Bering Strait?

2. On a map, try to point out: a) how Indians may have reached North America; b) some parts of North America where Indians lived before the white man came; c) some of the places where the Chumash made their homes.

3. Why are there no Chumash now?

4. What are some of the things an archaeologist a thousand years from now might find buried in your neighborhood?

5. Do some reading at the library to find out something about the China of 500 B.C.

6. Do some reading at the library about the history of Indians in Mexico. Be ready to report to the class about some part of it— their art, their ways of building, or their ways of treating illnesses.

7. What do such things as weather, water, and soil have to do with the way people live in different parts of the United States? Why are there fewer differences than there used to be between different parts of the country?

8. Chumash Boy made his dangerous journey the year Cabrillo died. How long ago was that?

9. Horses made a difference in the lives of the Plains Indians. What forms of travel have brought changes to the United States in the past three hundred years?

10. Why is it important for every person to have pride in himself? How do you think the Indians' pride and dignity can be best protected? In what ways has their sense of dignity been in danger of being destroyed?

11. What is meant by the words, "... they are the only true Americans among us"?

12. What are some of the "G.I." aids the United States government gives to citizens who have served in the armed forces? Why are those aids called "G.I." aids?

13. Look at the library for a book or magazine article about the Mohawk steel workers. Prepare a report for the class.

14. Put into your own words the statements made by the president of the National Indian Youth Council.

APPENDIX

LOOK-UPS

ancestral (an·ses′tral). Belonging to those members of a person's family who lived a long, long time ago.

archaeologist (ar·kē·ol′o·jist). A person who learns about the past by studying things that long-ago people left behind.

Asia (ā′zha). The largest piece of land in the world.

bait (bāt). Food or something else that helps to catch a fish or animal.

Bering Strait (ber′ing strāt). The body of water between Asia and Alaska.

Cabrillo (ka·brē′yo). The last name of the first white man known to have visited what is now California.

cactus (kak′tus). A plant with prickly scales.

Caribbean (kar′i·bē′an). Name of a sea.

channel (chan′el). A body of water that flows between two other bodies of water.

China (chī′na). A country in Asia.

Chumash (choo′mash). The name of an Indian tribe that once lived along the coast of California.

current (kur′ent). A body of water or stream of air that moves in a fixed direction.

custom (kus′tum). The way certain things are done, year after year.

dignity (dig′ni·ti). A quality of knowing one's worth as a human being and so as an important part of life and the world.

explorer (eks·plōr′er). One who travels in strange countries to learn about the place and the people.

fertilize (fur′ti·līz). To add something to soil in order to make it better for raising crops.

financial (fi·nan′shal). Having to do with money.

fire stick (fīr stik). A stick that is rubbed against wood or another stick in order to make fire.

flint (flint). A very hard rock that, when rubbed against metal, can make fire.

frontier (frun·tēr′). The land between the settled and the not yet settled parts of a country.

harpoon (har·poon′). A long spear used in killing whales.

heritage (her′i·tij). That which comes down to people from members of their group who lived before them.

India (in′di·a). A country in Asia.

Kolok (kō′lawk). The name of an Indian village.

mainland (mān′land′). A large body of land that has islands nearby.

mainstream (mān′strēm′). The main course of customs or events; the way of life of most people in a country.

mammoth (mam′uth). A very large animal, about fourteen feet high, that lived thousands of years ago.

Mexico (mek′si·kō). The country just south of the United States.

minority (mi·nor′i·ti). A group that is smaller in number than other groups.

missionaries (mish′un·er′iz). People sent by one country to try to get people in another country to follow the beliefs of the first country.

Mississippi (mis′i·sip′i). The name of a river that flows from northern Minnesota to the Gulf of Mexico.

Mohawks (mō′hoks). The name of an Indian tribe.

moon (mōōn). Used here to mean a month, or the time it takes the moon to go around the earth.

mush (mush). Indian meal that has been boiled in water.

nature (nā′tūr). All the things, not made by man, that make up the world we live in.

Navajos (nav′a·hōz). A group of Indians, most of whom live in the Southwest (Arizona, New Mexico, Utah, etc.).

Nimalala (nē′ma·la′la). The name of an Indian village.

original (ō·rij′i·nal). Having to do with the first or beginning of something.

potlatch (pot′lach′). A winter party, held each year by Indians in the Northwest, marked by the general giving of gifts.

poverty (pov′er·ti). The state of being very poor.

prehistoric (prē′his·tor′ik). Having to do with the time before any known history was written.

prey (prā). A person or animal that becomes the victim of another.

pueblos (pweb′lōz). Indian villages in the Southwest.

reservation (rez′er·vā′shun). Used here to mean a large piece of land that has been set aside for Indians who wish to live there.

resources (re·sōr′sez). Used here to mean the gifts of nature: water, soil, forests, wildlife, and minerals.

San Luis Obispo (san loo′is o·bis′pō). A place in the southwestern part of California, near the coast.

Santa Barbara (san′ta bar′ba·ra). A place on the southwest coast of California.

Shuku (shōō′kōō). The name of a village.

sweat house (swet hows). A place where some Indian men gathered to talk, smoke, bathe, and sometimes to sleep.

technical (tek′ni·kal). Having to do with some useful skill generally used in a particular field, such as mechanics.

tongue (tung). Used here to mean spoken language.

totem (tō′tem). A sign or symbol, such as a plant or animal, that an Indian family took as its own, rather in the way that some families in Europe had crests.

tribal (trīb′al). Having to do with a certain group called a tribe.

tribe (trīb). Used here to mean a group of Indians who lived in the same part of the country and spoke the same language.

Tukan (tōō′kan). The name of a village.

vanished (van′ishd). Used here to mean gone from the face of the earth.

Vikings (vī′kingz). Sailing men from the north of Europe who are believed to have visited North America some five hundred years or more before Columbus.

BOOKS TO READ

ARMER, LAURA A. *Waterless Mountain.* New York: David McKay., Inc., 1931.

This Newbery Medal winner brings insight and understanding to the feeling of many present-day Indian youths vis-a-vis their tribal heritage versus the white man's encroaching mores.

BAITY, ELIZABETH CHESLEY. *Americans Before Columbus.* New York: Viking Press, Inc., 1963.

Highly readable semifiction, laced with factual information and well illustrated with line drawings and photographs.

BLEEKER, SONIA. *The Navajo: Herders, Weavers, and Silversmiths.* New York: William Morrow & Co., Inc., 1958.

One of about a dozen excellent books by the same author, all dealing with American Indian tribes today and yesterday. Fictionalized material but highly detailed and informative.

BREWSTER, BENJAMIN. *The First Book of Indians.* New York: Franklin Watts, Inc., 1950.

Interesting account of tribal customs, dress, tools, play, et cetera, both in early and modern times.

BRINDZE, RUTH. *The Story of the Totem Pole.* New York, Vanguard Press, Inc., 1951.

Well-written, interesting stories of the totem poles of North American Indians.

BULLA, CLYDE ROBERT. *Squanto, Friend of the White Men.* New York: Thomas Y. Crowell Co., 1954.

Story portrait of the Indian who was taken to England to live but who returned to his homeland in time to welcome the Pilgrims and give them lessons in hunting, fishing, and planting crops.

CHRISTENSEN, GARDELL DANO. *Buffalo Kill.* New York: Thomas Nelson & Sons, 1959.

An exciting account of how the Plains Indians went hunting.

FALK, ELSA. *Fog Island.* Chicago: Wilcox & Follett, 1953.

Story of the Santa Barbara Channel Island Indians.

——. *Toki.* Chicago: Melmont Publishing Co., Inc., 1959.

Story of a Chumash Indian boy.

GLUBOK, SHIRLEY. *The Art of the North American Indian.* New York: Harper & Row, Publishers, 1964.

Largely pictorial, but the photographs (of masks, carvings, totem poles, et cetera) are accompanied by interesting, simply written text.

HOFSINDE, ROBERT. *The Indian Medicine Man.* New York: William Morrow & Co., Inc., 1966.

Description of the medicine men of the Sioux, Iroquois, Apache, Navajo, Ojibwa, and the Northwest Coast Indians.

——. *Indian Sign Language.* New York: William Morrow & Co., Inc., 1956.

> Children should enjoy these descriptions of Indian signs and how to make them, particularly since some of them portray contemporary English words, like "automobile."

LaFarge, Oliver. *The American Indian.* New York: Golden Press, Inc., 1960.

> Good material, well illustrated.

Martin, Charles M. *Monsters of Old Los Angeles.* New York: The Viking Press, 1950.

> The story of the fabulous animals that roamed California in prehistoric times.

Mason, Bernard S. *The Book of Indian Crafts and Costumes.* New York: Ronald Press Co., 1946.

> Interesting do-it-yourself presentations of the fashioning of war bonnets, moccasins, necklaces, drums, et cetera.

McNeer, May, and Ward, Lynd. *The American Indian Story.* New York: Ariel Books, 1963.

> Handsomely illustrated book that presents historical information in the guise of delightful stories about Indian heroes and notable events. Two stories, or chapters, deal with present-day Indians.

Schoor, Gene. *The Jim Thorpe Story.* New York: Julian Messner, Inc., 1962.

> A biographical tribute to a great human being who was also a magnificent athlete.

Stevens, Mary Ellen. *Little Cloud and the Great Plains Hunters 15,000 Years Ago.* Chicago: Reilly & Lee Co., 1962.

> The Texas Panhandle as it might have appeared to an Indian child of prehistoric times. An interesting story marked by authentic anthropological detail.

Tunis, Edwin. *Indians.* Cleveland: World Publishing Co., 1959.

> Dependable reference material for project-minded youngsters reading at fourth-grade level or above. Well and profusely illustrated.

Wellman, Paul I. *Indian Wars and Warriors West.* Boston: Houghton Mifflin Co., 1959.

> Objective accounts of some aspects of the conflict between Indians and the white invaders, with special attention to heroes and villains on both sides.

White, Anne Terry. *Indians and the Old West.* New York: Golden Press, Inc., 1958.

> Accurate information, simply and interestingly presented and beautifully illustrated.

SOUTHERN UTAH STATE COLLEGE
CEDAR CITY, UTAH 84720

3 3079 00100 4758

Curr
428.4
F457a
no.1